Letterland

Phonics Practice 3

24 pages

Decodable text

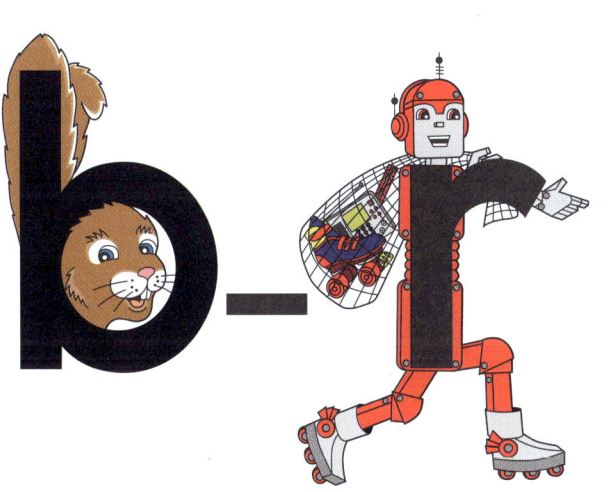

Contains:

Adjacent consonants
with l: b-l, c-l, f-l, g-l, p-l
with r: b-r, c-r, d-r, f-r, g-r, p-r, t-r
with s   s-c, s-k, s-l, s-m, s-n, s-p, s-t, s-w
endings n-t, n-d, -nk

Consonant digraphs
ch, sh, th, th, wh, ph

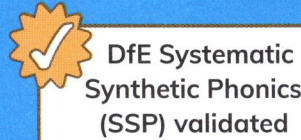

DfE Systematic Synthetic Phonics (SSP) validated

Name:

b-l, c-l, f-l, g-l, p-l Consonant plus l

  +

1. Read the words, then join each word to the matching picture. Write the words again.

clap

flock    *clap*

blocks  _____

flag  _____

plan  _____

2. Write **b-l**, **c-l** or **f-l** on the lines and trace the letters to make the words under each picture.

__iff __ock __ack __ap

3. Unscramble the words and write them on the blank blocks.

u	m	p	l	🍇				
l	o	c	k	🕐				
p	l	g	u	💡				
a	c	k	l	b				
l	f	a	g	🚩				
l	u	p	s	✚				

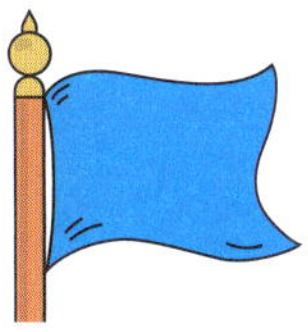

b-l, c-l, f-l, g-l, p-l   Consonant plus l

4. Read the words. Then colour the star next to the matching picture.

A black clock.

A red flag.

A big blob.

The plug is in.

A flat hat.

He is glad the sock is black.

5. Read the sentence and circle the picture that matches.

Ben has not got the blocks.

6. Write the words in the spaces to finish the sentence and match the picture.

| flip-flops   glad   blob   glum |

The sand is hot.

He is ____ he has

____-____ on.

b-r, c-r, d-r, f-r, g-r, p-r, t-r **Consonant plus r**

1. Read the words, then join each word to the matching picture. Write the words again.

drip

crab

dress   drip

frog

press

2. Write **b-r**, **c-r** or **t-r** on the lines and trace the letters to make the words under each picture.

___ip   ___ick   ___ack

3. Unscramble the words and write them on the blank blocks.

| s | e | s | r | d | (dress)

| t | a | r | ck | (track)

| r | c | p | o | (crop)

| u | ck | r | t | (truck)

| r | m | u | d | (drum)

| o | g | r | f | (frog)

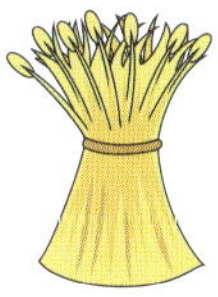

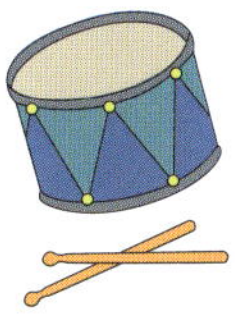

b-r, c-r, d-r, f-r, g-r, p-r, t-r   Consonant plus r

4. Read the words. Then colour the star next to the matching picture.

A red crab.

Lots of bricks.

A duck and a drum.

A frog on Fred.

Yes. Press it.

Gran is at the track.

s-c, s-k, s-l, s-n, s-p, s-t, s-w   s plus consonant

s +

1. Slide Sammy Snake up to the words by tracing over the dotted lines. Write in his letter on the lines. Then read the words from left to right and match them to the pictures.

_s_wing

_top

_nap

_pill

_kid

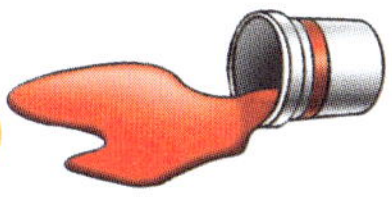

2. Write **s-k**, **s-p** or **s-w** on the lines to make the word to match the pictures.

___im   ___ip   ___in   ___id

3. Unscramble the words and write them on the blank blocks.

s e l m l

p s l l i

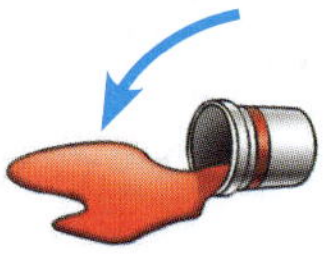

s i c t k

a c k s n

o t s p

t a s m p

| s-c, s-k, s-l, s-n, s-p, s-t, s-w | **s plus consonant** |

4. Read the words. Then colour the star next to the matching picture.

He can spin.

He can skip.

I spot six stamps.

Nick has a snack.

Fred can swim.

She smells a slug!

5. Read the sentence and circle the picture that matches. Then write the sentence below.

Sam can swim at this spot.

___ ___ ___ ___ ___ ___ ___

6. Write these words in the spaces to finish the sentences and match the picture.

| skip swing stop slip |

Sam can ___ .

He cannot ___ .

He must hold on

and not ___ off!

Review - Blending adjacent consonants

1. Think about the words in the box. Write them in the spaces where they belong. Some may belong in more than one group.

skid	crab	spin	sloth
sting	swing	swim	skip
smash	frog	grin	slug
slam	flip	crush	clap

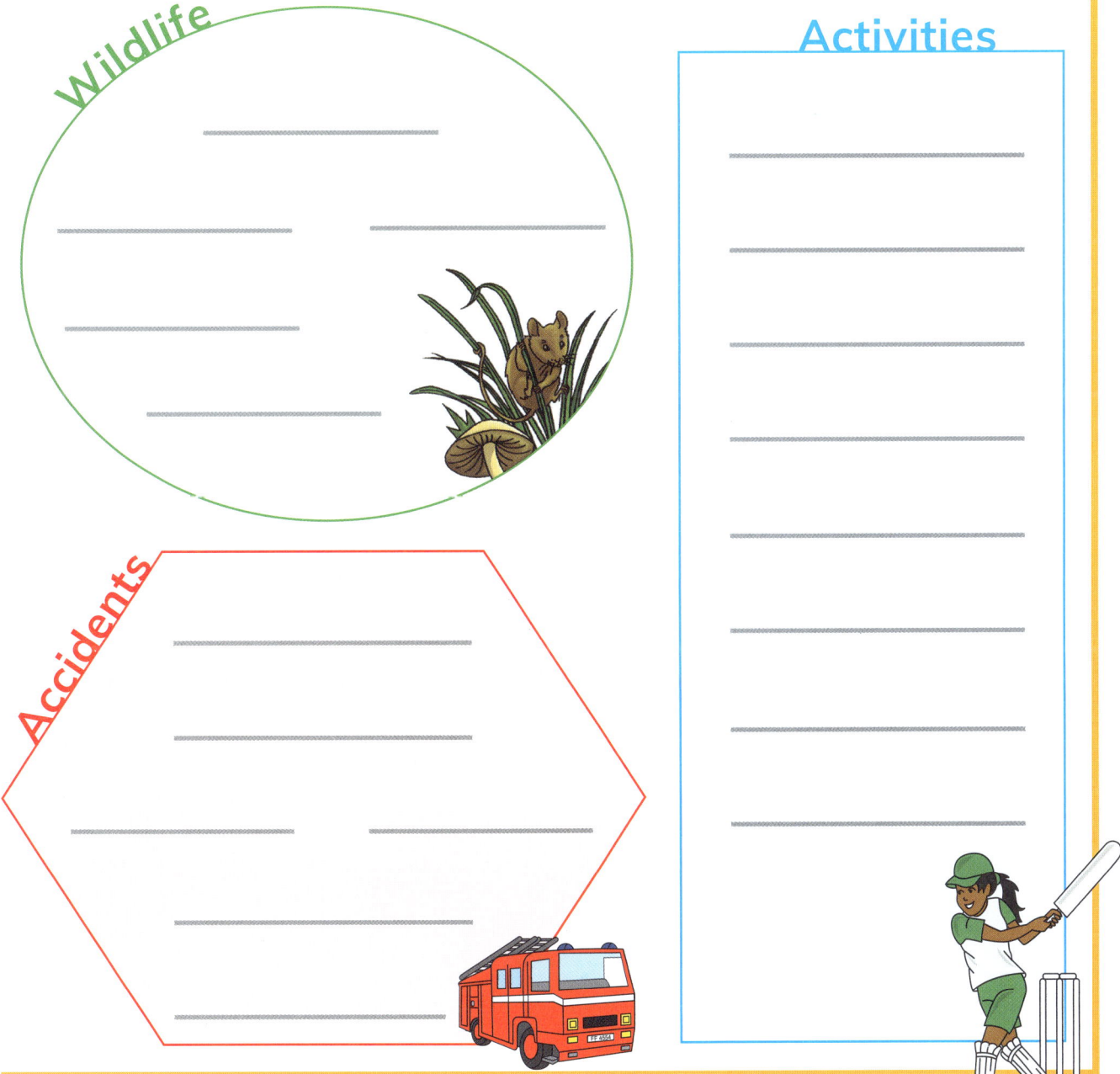

Wildlife

Activities

Accidents

13

Review - Blending adjacent consonants

1. Read the questions and put a tick in the correct boxes to answer.

Yes **No**

Can a crab skip?

Can a clock swim?

Can a man clap?

2. Fill in the missing words. Then read the sentences with expression. Add the clap as an action, too!

A _____ sits on a _____. Clap! It jumps off.

A _____ sits on a _____. Clap! It jumps off.

A _____ sits on a _____. Snap! It jumps off.

Final n-d, n-k and n-t

1. Write **n-d**, **n-k** or **n-t** on the lines to end the pictured words.

a___   sa___   po___   si___

pa___   dri___   be___   i___

2. Write these words in the spaces to finish the sentences and match the picture.

| sink   tank   pink |

I will drop the _____ cup

in the _____.

It will _____.

15

Clever Cat and Harry Hat Man **ch** as in chip

1. Fill in the spaces with **ch** or **sh**. Read the words. Then join them to the pictures.

___in

___ell

___ick

___op

___op

fi___

Talking Tess, Clever Cat and Harry **tch** as in catch

1. Fill in the missing letters **tch** in these words.

ca___

pi___

ma___

16

sh as in shop

Sammy Snake and Harry Hat Man

1. Read the two words below the picture. Circle the word that matches the picture.

ship   shut

shack   shin

axes   ashes

kick   cash

2. Read the sentence that goes with this picture twice. Then write it on the lines below.

I got Shep at the pet shop.

17

Talking Tess and Harry Hat Man **th** as in that

1. Use the words below to fill in the spaces in the sentences.

> This   Shep

____ is ____ and me.

> that   She

____ naps in ____ shed.

2. Finish the words below, trace and read the sentences.

__is man chops __e logs.

__en he sits and rests.

th as in thing   Talking Tess and Harry Hat Man

1. Read the seven words. Choose and write the four correct words to match the pictures.

thin   path   moth
maths   thick   chin   bath

_____   _____   _____   _____

2. Choose the correct words from the top of the page to complete these sentences.

Ed has _____ legs.

The duck has _____ legs.

The _____ is on the cloth.

19

Walter Walrus and Harry Hat Man

wh as in when

1. Read the two words beneath each picture. Circle the word that matches.

whiff   whoff   whack   whap

whozz   whizz   whisk   whosk

2. Look at the picture. Then read questions. Colour the star next to the question that best matches the picture.

When will he drink?

When will he get up?

When will he sing?

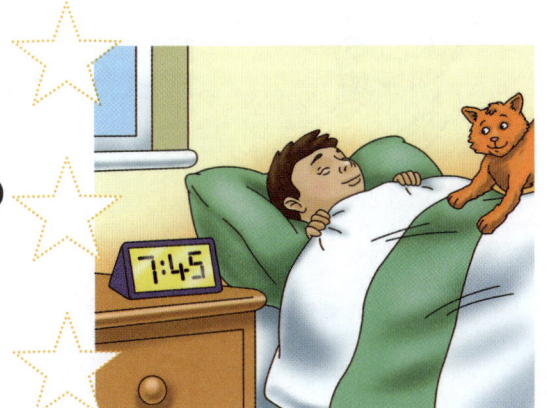

3. Use the words below to fill in the spaces. Then tick the correct answer.

Think! _____ gift is the best?

A _____ ☐   A lamp ☐

| whisk   Which |

wh as in who   Walter Walrus and Harry Hat Man

1. Can you hear Walter or Harry saying their sound in the words below? Copy the words on to the lines in the correct box.

| whisk   whom   which   whose |

when

who

Peter Puppy and Harry Hat Man

ph as in phone

1. Draw a line around all the **ph** words in the word search below. They go across and down.

b	r	s	d	t	q	i
s	d	e	o	y	j	q
c	u	v	l	w	s	v
g	r	a	p	h	w	p
e	d	f	h	g	o	h
i	j	k	i	m	t	y
p	h	o	n	i	c	s

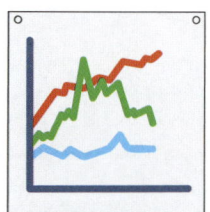
graph

dolphin

phonics

2. Match the sentence to the picture.

This is a graph. •   •

This is a dolphin. •   •
abcdefghi
jklmnopq
rstuvwxyz

This is the alphabet. •   •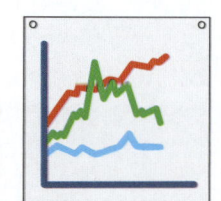

22

Review th, wh, ph

1. Fill the gaps with the correct words.

> thing   What   dolphin   that

_____ is that _____?

I think _____ is a fin.

It is a _____!

2. Draw a funny thing in the box. Then answer the question.

What is that thing?

_____

How to use this book

On each page, read the instructions to the children. Name all the pictures with them. Let them try and read all the words in the exercises themselves, as they are decodable. The workbooks are designed to consolidate and extend the teaching content of the Letterland *Phonics Teacher's Guide*.

Blending with adjacent consonants
This workbook's focus is on blending and segmenting adjacent consonants. It also teaches common digraphs. This enables them to read hundreds more short vowel words and consolidate their decoding and spelling skills.

Skills covered include:
- phonemic awareness
- decoding skills
- word building
- reading for meaning
- sentence completion
- using words in context when writing.

It is important to use this workbook:
- when children are not tired
- when there are no background distractions
- for short periods of time
- with plenty of praise and encouragement.

Correct handwriting positions

   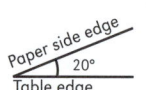 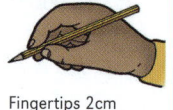

Left-hander

Fingertips 4cm from tip of pencil

Paper side edge 30° Table edge
Elbows off the table
Feet on floor

Right-hander

Paper side edge 20° Table edge
Chair slightly tilted
Feet on floor

Fingertips 2cm from tip of pencil

You may also like:

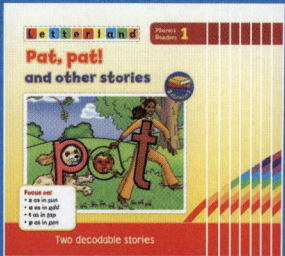 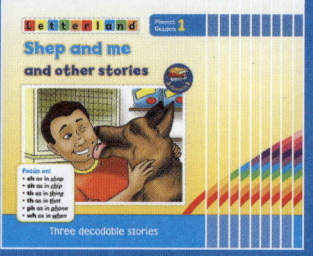

Published by Letterland International Ltd.
8/10 South Street, Epsom, Surrey, KT18 7PF, UK
© Letterland International 2021
10 9 8 7 6 5 4 3 2 1

ISBN: 978-1-78248-552-0
Product Code: TP67

LETTERLAND™ is a trademark of Letterland International Ltd.
Printed in China.

All rights reserved. No part of this publication may be reproduced, stored in a retrieval system, or transmitted in any form or by any means, electronic, mechanical, photocopying, recording or otherwise, without the prior permission of the Publisher or a licence permitting restricted copying in the United Kingdom issued by the Copyright Licensing Agency Ltd, 90 Tottenham Court Road, London W1P 0LP. British Library Cataloguing in Publication Data. A catalogue record for this book is available from the British Library.

Sassoon Infant is a typeface designed for children learning to read and write.
© Adrian Williams Design Ltd

Written and designed by Lisa Holt
Consultant: Lyn Wendon, originator of Letterland

See our full range at: www.letterland.com

Please Note: These practice books match the teaching order in the Letterland *Phonics Teacher's Guide*.

For those who wish to follow a different teaching order the practice books can be used flexibly.

Code: TP67
ISBN 978-1-78248-552-0

9 781782 485520